Let The We
Be Settled

Alex Green

Let The West Coast Be Settled

ISBN – 13: 978-1-904551-97-3

A CIP record for this title is available from the British Library.

Published by tall-lighthouse press.

Acknowledgements and thanks to:

Roland Belcher, David Porter, Jesse Michaels, Yvonne Prinz, Dan Coshnear, Robb and Darla Benson, Justin Currie, Paul Gleason, Gareth Lewis and Azadeh

CONTENTS

The Wide Gates Of The Lowlands

The closing night of the campus production of *The Crucible* you went to Cathy Hickman's party still in character: the long white wig, the tattered black poncho, the thick grey makeup that made it look like you were hundreds of years old, from the moon and made of ashes. It was the same night they found the body of the sitar player in the hills above the golf course. For years he'd been performing midnight surgeries in a dark warehouse for anyone who wanted a thing done so much, it didn't matter if it was done terribly. When it was over, the patient would have to walk up the embankment and across the long empty parking lot to their car, their body stinging with errors. Then the woozy ride home, the swerve in the stomach, the crude stitches weak with blood and losing their grip. They found him pretty much in pieces—dragged apart in the darkness for miles. At the party you tried everything—you even did an impression of the puppet from that sitcom, but Cathy Hickman still wouldn't let you touch her. She sat far away from you on the couch and talked about waterskiing. And Italy. And a guy who was coming home from the Air Force. Later in your dorm room you watched a metal band on TV play a concert in the Philippines. You stood in the bathroom and scraped the cakey makeup off your face while they played a song about burning Troy to the ground. It fell away in the sink in big white clumps that collapsed under the hot water and dissolved in a long, grey stream. You looked in the mirror and were relieved to see that you were still young. It was the last time you would ever be that lucky.

Gene Clark

Gene Clark sunk your dad's boat off the coast of Regatta Del Mar. Your dad was so mad you could hear him yelling a mile from the shore where you were surfing. His voice cut through the waves like something terrible and sharp. *I don't care who he is*, he screamed, *he owes me now*. But you were sure if your dad ever heard Gene Clark's voice roll under a tambourine or glide inside the jangle of a Rickenbacker, he'd change his mind and admit that it was he who owed Gene Clark something. The next day they met in your dad's office, and afterwards Gene Clark walked to the water looking like he had been sad about the same thing since 1967. You followed him to the pier where he sat down on the edge; the boats of the cliff millionaires swayed together like royal swans and a plane dragged a chain across the sky. Gene Clark's hair hung in his face and he never looked up. A guy in a suit brought him something to drink and a stack of papers to sign. A blonde girl with an accent joined them and rubbed Gene Clark's shoulders. You could see yourself in the reflection of her hair; you memorized that species of light. At dusk the surfers walked in from the fading glow of the coastline. They left the beach in bursts of electricity but they came back as silhouettes, and that was when you were sure the world would soon be over; everything would sink and nothing, not even the crush of summer in Santa Monica, would ever matter again.

The Pounding Waves Soaring Lightly

The rock climber loves the girl whose boyfriend was killed by a shark. But no matter what he does he'll always be in second place to the dead surfer who, in his last seconds, stumbled through the waves and back to the beach, blood surging from his side, just to say goodbye to her. Nothing can top that, but he keeps trying anyway: he tells her about sleeping on the side of a mountain, falling fifty feet into a jagged city of rocks, and how one time his knee exploded in so many pieces, the surgeons needed to bring in books to remember what it was supposed to look like. She tells him she's glad he's alive and falls asleep with her head on his chest in a way that feels patronizing. He feels his climbing scars glowing in embarrassment. No trial will ever be enough if later he's able to stand around at a party and say, *It was night, it was freezing, I had to hold my head together with a bungee cord.* But he knows the real problem is that he's lived too long. All he can do is imagine the dead boyfriend and the shark missing each other by miles. He pictures him walking unharmed from the water, sticking his board in the sand and lying down next to her. He says stupid things about the waves and the weather while she nods disinterestedly behind her sunglasses and reads a book about a blue wolf in an Arctic town. If only he had lived he would have been powerless and without the charge of a tragedy. If only he had lived, everyone else would have had a chance.

Last Broadcast, Avery Island

The band in the backyard busks behind the barbeque
and the actor closes his eyes and wishes his birthday
wasn't over so soon. Next to him is his girlfriend, the one
who reads philosophy and loves to explain how the heart
has a seasonal migration, whether it wants one or not.
When the sun sets and the patio and the pool turn to sepia,
it's like watching a memory being made. It's been that
kind of a good day. But he doesn't know he'll be dead
soon, on the ski slopes, and very badly. The ski patrol will
look down the mountain and slowly shake their heads; the
body will be loaded into the ambulance with not the
slightest trace of urgency and the driver won't even start
the engine until he hears the last minute of a hockey game
he doesn't even really care about. These things will
happen. But first she listens to a song about falling in love
on ferries and across long kitchens in Hungary. It's so
beautiful, the girl feels the next decade swell under her
ribcage with such a great dose of promise it makes her
lose her memory. It's the kind of day she'll only
remember years later, when it's summer and it isn't, when
she thinks it's love, but it's not. When she realizes that
everything since then has been nothing special.

Highlights From *Under The Sod*

In the novel *Under The Sod* there are no characters in the
first 338 pages. There's a great deal of vegetation, a few
passages about the ocean and a long chapter about fog.
The first line of the fog chapter is "The fog is the quietest
species of weather." and the last line is "One can be
mauled in secret." Finally, there's the appearance of a
painter wandering through a city plagued by such a
terrible curse, it will never be lifted no matter how much
somebody loves somebody else. For the next 654 pages
the fog stops, the landscape gets considerably greener
and people do things: a wrecked sailor with a bony
compass for a heart wheezes against the boiling waves, a
princess disguised as a swordsmith cries into the fire and
in a tavern there's a fistfight between a playwright and
another playwright. One of them thinks it's about the bill,
the other thinks it's about a girl but it's really about
neither and it ends very badly for both of them. The book
then lapses into what critics have described as "deep
pastoralia": boys chase girls through meadows, birds
glide through laurel trees and a man stands on a hill
overlooking the valley and plays a wood instrument that
makes flowers open so wide, their petals arch their backs
and snap off in mid-air. The next section is too long for
most people; it's the kind of dense, slow motion prose that
makes you want to kill yourself. The 2,098 pages of this
section can be best summarized in one sentence: a man
crawls on his stomach across the riverbank. In the book's
final ten pages, there's a clash between two armies, it's
night forever, nobody's happy, etc. The book ends at
dusk, in a coat of half-light and shadows, the sky a layer of
crimson, the horizon laid with murder. Below the cliffs
something opens and closes its jaws. Somebody sits in the
darkness making sketches of cities. Leaning back on the
deck, a sailor with a fatal spider bite has to wait for weeks
to never make it home.

California Divorce

At Makena beach on Maui, seven people are attacked by a shark over the course of nine days. It could be different sharks, but that's not the point. The point is they've been married three days and now the honeymoon is ruined. She's sad about the places they could have gone, but she mourns Paris the most. *Honfleur, Gleyre*, she tells him. *Entreat, Bougival, The Hotel des Roches-Noires.* He says he's only heard of the last one. That night in the disco, she finally admits he's not a good dancer. Later, when she sleeps, he longs for the nasty thrills of old crimes. Six days later they still haven't gone in the water. She watches a rerun of a sitcom from 1982 in Portuguese. He loses one thousand seventy-three dollars in a shell game to a guy in a hat whose hands move like chopper blades. In the afternoon they walk around the suite with their backs to each other. It's the kind of Sunday afternoon that makes you want to kill someone. Weeks later, when the shark is finally gone, no one will really know. There won't be a meeting or a memo, it will just be a guess, a turn of the instinct that says *Now*. After that, it's hard to say what will happen next. In the meantime they keep going to restaurants and just sitting there. At dusk, surfers paddle in and dissolve on the beach, strumming acoustic guitars before twitching fires. When it gets dark, couples walk away from each other across parking lots; sharks burst from shipwrecks and start looking.

When He Wound His Arms About The Waters

At the Olympics in London, the swimmer who lived up the
street stood on the blocks in a black suit and goggles. His
body had rows of muscles like the kind you saw on the
backs of jaguars in nature documentaries. It made you
wish you had spent time getting great at something. Your
city had stood still for him all summer: hardware stores
and high schools were covered in banners, there were
parades with marching bands and girls throwing batons
through fire, and the coffee shop named a latte after him.
You were supposed to want him to win, but before the
race the profile of the guy from Belgium whose house had
burned down was too compelling for you to take sides too
quickly. His dad had fallen asleep smoking, the house
went up in flames and the family barely escaped. The clip
ended with the swimmer and his father talking about
healing and starting over, while passing a puppy from lap
to lap. And there were other stories, too: the Canadian
had a bad heart that was due to explode before he turned
thirty; the Russian was an orphan who had witnessed a
murder and the guy from France was blind in one eye.
When they jumped from the blocks and starting slicing
through the water, you couldn't tell them apart anymore;
the Belgian with the burning house, the Canadian with the
hourglass heart, the local Olympian who got your sister
and her best friend pregnant within a week of each other.
You held your breath and felt stupid about the ways you
planned to be famous: playing drums for The Young
Murder Executives, escaping from handcuffs underwater
surrounded by sharks, or stealing your brother's
girlfriend, or driving to another state and writing a
screenplay about how when you're madly in love you'll
destroy anyone. But suddenly all you wanted was to live
through a horrible disaster and talk on national television
about starting over in a furnished apartment. You wanted
to stare into the interviewer's eyes and say, *after the
explosion I became the fastest man in the world.*

Blurry World

Even though he graduates from Julliard with flash and promise, when the actor moves to L.A. the only part he gets is on a made-for-television movie, playing a lifeguard who rides a motorcycle and does lousy things late at night. The ratings are so high it's turned into a weekly series called *Malibu Silk*. He tries to make the character complicated and tragic, but there's only so much he can convey when most of the scenes take place in a hot tub. Frustrated, he takes control of the direction and in one scene instead of taking off the Senator's daughter's bra and kissing her over the sound of synth reggae, he stares up at the sky and delivers a monologue about dying in the rain. Shooting the scene takes most of the day. The real director could care less—he sits smoking in a chair with his headphones on, listening to an industrial band from 1987 whose singer was killed in a bar after a disagreement about a girl he'd only known for two days. The director has rabies and is weak from the fifth round of shots; he's barely eaten in weeks and falls asleep at traffic lights. Like a low, dense fog, a flush has permanently settled on him, making his clothes sticky all day. A bat had flown through his bedroom window and bit him on the arm before finding its way back into the night. *Do you still have the bat*, the vet had asked. *I never had the bat*, he had said. *It'd be better if we had the bat*, the vet said. The shots turned his blood hot and thick; it made him feel like something big and heaving that drags itself across swamps. When people ask him what's wrong, he's never been able to explain it right, no matter how many times he says, *gothic fever, terrible moon, the sky wet with signals.*

Giverny Floodlands

Until the girl who called you in the middle of the night and said, *I have a fever because of this thing,* slides from the dark embers of your arms, you'll always be standing on the porch in the rain, listening to the bells of the university hold their breath between each ring. Soon there will be an undergraduate with an oar that can slice water into obedient strips. Soon there will be a boy who can make all the girls turn colors. Somebody will borrow a boat one weekend and you'll never see her again. The press of the campus and all the deep semester voodoo makes you think there are too many things in your mouth. Soon it really will be winter; the frozen faculty will move slowly to meetings with the crooked shoulders of a Greek Chorus, and out every window you'll study the lights of the freeway, trying to spot a car crash. You can already hear the mix of metal scraping against the engine; the static of crushed speakers, the wild hiss of wires, the flickering signal in a city of radios.

The Song That Was Playing
While The Woods Were Burning

Bill Tilden didn't go to the tennis tournament in Australia. Because his knee was shattered, he smoked cigarettes in the backyard of the summer mansion and listened to phonograph records of sad songs played by big bands. He kept the volume low so it always sounded distant; like a girl crying on the 8th floor of a hotel, or the bells of a cathedral in the background of a scratchy phone call from Lyon. He felt too old for revenge, too broken to roam the late night cities of the world drinking black market cocktails and tripping down alleys holding someone else's knife. News of the Russian acrobats' caravan exploding in the forest reached him by butler in the twilight. In the wake of the grim reports he wondered if at least one of the unbreakable boys with springing limbs found his way through the flames, backflipped above the trees and somersaulted to secret safety. *Great tragedy,* he thought, *should always offer at least one splendid thing.* Night came in an ashy layer and he let it pull him under its big dirty cape. The woods were on fire with acrobats and once again love had let itself get turned back into smoke. Like a closed fist blasted open, his knee floated up and down his leg with shards of bones that would never find their way back to each other ever again.

A Person's Guide To The Rest Of Summer

After your son is attacked by a shark, you sit in the waiting
room of the hospital that overlooks the ocean and think:
This is what a vacation looks like when it's not working. You
can see the nurse's tan lines glowing under their
uniforms; when they walk by they smell like suntan oil
and summer in America. The one you've had your eye on
comes over to you; she looks like the actress from the
television show *F.B.I. Beach Patrol.* You remember one
episode when she chased a bank robber down the beach
and broke both his legs; the bills flew loose from the sack
and went limp in the waves. The nurse tells you it's bad,
but it's good your son is young. She explains the
problems with the mouths of sharks and how the scar will
be a rickety seam of teeth. After she leaves, you notice
how the sand has hardened all over your body; when you
move it cracks down your back and across your stomach.
You spit in your palms to get rid of the chalky thickness.
Next to you a surfer with a shattered elbow that splinters
out of his bicep like a mangled umbrella sways back and
forth. Water from his hair sprays lightly on your cheek
and you want to hold him like a healer, turn his bones to
magic, loose him back into the waves.

The World And What To Do With It

At the end of the semester it still isn't winter; the trees,
brown and folded, hang off the side of the hill like dead
parachutists. Experts say there won't be clouds for weeks;
the endless sheets of blue sky are predicted to never
stop. It's warm, it's dry and across the city one by one,
houses wrapped in Christmas lights catch fire and burn to
the ground. Some people walk around slow and stunned
while others sit on the hoods of their broken down cars
that leak fluids from open wounds in their engines. Across
the city no one is really sure if it's an emergency, so they
stay on the beach, vibrating with volleyballs and radios
and surfboards. And even though every now and then
they get kind of nervous, worries can't last for long under
such a winning streak of sun. You turn your grades in and
catch your breath at the knees of the university. Later in
your old sailboat you sit in the water and wait for anything
resembling a breeze. On the radio the weatherman has
now resorted to shorthand and just says, *more of this*. You
sprinkle ice into a glass, pour lemonade over it and listen
to its bones snap across the harbor. You remember a
story about a spaceman who floated away from the radar
and disappeared for weeks behind the moon. *I thought I
was dead*, he said years later, *and I thought it was going to
stay that way forever.*

West Coast Wreckage

The singer for the Young Murder Executives doesn't know
how to break up with his girlfriend. He thinks about
writing her a note or having a serious dinner with her
under the soft lights of a restaurant by the water, but
secretly wishes he could just disappear quietly with the
actress from Spain. Looking around their apartment he
should be thinking, *This is what life looks like when you let
the air out. This is a head start on the aftermath.* But instead
he leans over the balcony and tries to read a book about
something that happened in Turkey in 1923. Below he
sees the surfing instructor talking to a girl. He stares at
her reflection in the glare of the board—she's made of
silver, she's outlined in italics; she looks like someone
who's been living forever or who's been dead for years.
Down the promenade a juggler throws up chainsaws and
bowling balls and fiery torches. A kid with an acoustic
guitar plays an old Irish song about boats and wars and
the open hearts of the dead; he's not sure which one is
making him feel worse. While he waits for her to come
home he watches a show on television about things in
Australia that can kill you. A spider with the kind of
muscles usually found on plastic action figures breaks
open a beetle like an egg. It throbs in and out of the black
shell until it eases into a liquid.

At The End Of The Movie The Guy

But before that, the fog would come out of the mineral
factory and below the dock in italics a boat swayed like
perhaps, perhaps. And in your American stutter you lapse
into the moment of a thousand years, where you are
driving down a freeway towards the ocean, holding a
phone against your glowing jaw, and wearing sunglasses
that airbrush everything into sepia footage from a '60s
surf film. On the beach a couple holding hands run
towards the water, a surfer shines his board into a still-
life, and you are stunned at how quickly you have
forgotten the name of the girl who drowned. But you do
remember how they churned through the water, pulled
her from the choppy palace and turned her body in
circles, like they were smothering a fire. And when they
slid her suit all the way down her body, you felt the sunset
on your shoulders break down your back like decades.
You stood behind the coast guard who had collapsed over
her in measured sobs, and even though you were only a
boy, you could feel her count to ten and kiss the air
between his lips; and you could hear a man on the radio
whose house had disappeared in the flood tell a reporter
he was tired of talking about water.

Davenport Before and After

In a small town by the ocean the movie theater closes at
8:30, whether the movie is over or not.

Strobe Light Retrospective

Nobody could believe the rabbi murdered his wife, but it
was true. He drowned her in the big hot tub in their
backyard, made a quiet phone call to the police and
waited for them out front. *These are the things we do as
people*, he had said. You were fourteen and didn't know
rabbis killed their wives—you didn't know they had hot
tubs, either. All summer at Temple you sat behind Sheyna
Dumas and watched the tan lines brighten across her
back. From shoulder to shoulder you imagined crossing
that golden bridge. The new rabbi was young and tried to
sound too cool; he talked a lot about baseball and quoted
a rock band no one had liked in years. You only paid
attention to the cantor who sang songs from a centerless
alphabet. Listening to her voice climb and burst in
triumphant triple axles made you feel swollen with
promise and destiny. At night in your parents' pool you
floated on your back and made up fake Yiddish
constellations: Shlomo the magician, Harel the racquetball
champion. The season was almost over; in the water you
felt the heat fading beneath you. You stayed up late
watching talk shows and nature documentaries. In one, a
lost kit fox traveled the Arctic tundra alone for weeks. You
cried when he made it home. Sometimes you imagined
the rabbi small in his cell and pacing away the rest of his
life, but not very often. You were about to start high
school and had begun to think of Temple as a place where
you used to go. All you could really think about was how
in a few weeks you would be slow dancing with girls; how
you would slowly step under the strobe light that splashed
over the gym floor and follow the beaming circles of the
dappled path, blinking a trail in front of you like an
answer key.

Australian Divorce

Because you are so far behind, you decide to take your
marriage Pass/Fail. And then that's it. Sometimes you go
to work, but mostly you surf Eade Point, then sit on the
beach and watch people try to talk to each other. It won't
get any better but it doesn't matter; by now you are used
to the sharks that move under the relay of radios, the slip
of the surf in a summer of cheaters.

Why You'll Never Live In Ithaca

On the porch you tell a girl a stupid story about Easter
and the fire you started in the kitchen by accident. It's a
relief when bad things become funny. It's a relief when
you can sit around a table with a group of friends and say
the car just kept going over the cliff. But it's terrible when
you remember the chocolate rabbits dissolving in their
boxes, the flames throwing open the cabinet doors and
crawling under the floor and exploding under the
refrigerator like a heart bursting inside a chest.
Sometimes things don't get to be okay because they're
still happening. Like weeks after your brother's boat
disappeared and they pulled him from the surf, water
poured out of his body like it had been the only thing
keeping him alive. On the eighth floor of a hotel she takes
off her clothes and angles over you, and you want
everything that's about to happen to stay that way: let the
girl in the blouse hover, let the stereo stay broken, let the
music inside keep holding its breath.

Why A Chokehold Only Works
If The Person Is Standing Near You

On the news you never hear about someone who is good
at karate saving the day; banks get robbed, cars get
stolen and buildings explode, but nothing is ever clarified
by a black belt who can kick the air into stars and snap
limbs behind his back without even turning. You keep
waiting for a crime to be derailed by a reverse rear punch
or a knife-hand strike, but it never happens; you wonder if
it's because everyone's too busy practicing karate in strip
malls, so there's no one around to kick guns into the night.
Once you signed up for a martial arts class, but in the first
few minutes you tore your groin so badly you felt the
muscle split from the bone and orbit violently below your
abdomen. Driving home, the pain vibrated in the new
pocket of empty space where something used to be
connected to something else. When you got there you
needed the retired magician with emphysema to help you
out of your car and into your house. You fell asleep on the
couch to a cooking show where everybody cheered when
alcohol and cheese got added to pasta sauce. When you
woke up, the magician was still there, sitting next to you
and passing coins over his fingers; you watched the silver
rise from nowhere, stand up like wheels and roll down his
wrists. The ballet of coins moved to the beat of what little
breath he had left. You could hear how the gears of his
lungs had snapped—you imagined them wet and frayed,
dangling over the boneless galaxies of his throat.

Maple Through The Breakers

The famous magician wants to tell the girl he's not that
great a magician—got lucky once with some knives and
built a career on a chorus of blades that no one seems to
ever tire of. In the darkness her blinking skirt flashes like
a map of dying stars. In front of the café the syrup truck
has exploded; the driver stands with the police, shaking
his head and holding his hands far apart to show either
the intensity of the explosion or how close he was to
getting home. The syrup hangs thick and slow over
everything—the trees, the street, the windows of the
café—and in a boneless drag it pulls the night into
bronze. It reminds the magician that the girl has come
from nowhere and he doesn't want her to ever go back.
The tires of his car barely manage the new heaviness of
the road and the wipers stretch golden streaks across the
windshield. They take the bridge to the ocean and later in
front of a bonfire he juggles swords, swallows bullets and
tears up cards that he pulls whole from the flames seconds
later. In the air there's still the smell of maple and fire and
as decades of stars fall from her skirt and back into the
glowless galaxies between the night, he thinks, *we are
either out of time or we aren't.*

They'll Know When You're Gone

The people in the ad for the health club don't actually belong to the health club. The girl on the elliptical trainer is a singer from Portland who has written hundreds of songs about dead surfers. At night she stays awake listening to her hermit crab shift in his tank, and imagines someone is on the roof with a knife and a bad knee. The guy with the towel around his neck stars in movies about lifeguards and rock stars and people pretending to be rich and terrible in Malibu. He holds the record for most scenes shot in a hot tub (124) and most consecutive movies that have gone direct to video (57). The thing that troubles him most in the world is that he knows exactly how much time he has left to look carelessly handsome. The kids in the pool aren't related or even friends; in real life they eat candy the color of electricity, do sports that mostly bore them and play video games about murder in outer space. Not only is the couple in the sauna not married, the picture wasn't even shot with them in the same room. She does print work for clothing catalogues from Vermont, but her fake husband's shirtless picture was stolen from an ad in a European hospitality magazine and photoshopped in to make it look like they were together. The real guy will never find this out. He'll continue to play a ski instructor on a German soap opera and he'll keep touring with his synth pop band, Klaberjass. Their hit "Dance Ceramics" will stay atop the charts for a record number of weeks (34). A staggering number of people will fall in love to it on the dance floor (12,987). One of these couples will break up and the boy will take it very badly. He'll tell someone his heart feels a house that has slid down a muddy riverbank and collapsed into the rapids. They won't know what to say. Years later he'll write an essay called "The Trouble With Love Is You Never Forget How You Thought You Felt." It will be published in an esteemed journal and the cover will be a drawing of a robot with a heart over its head offering a flower to a seal. The drawing will become very famous. It will make people feel terrible and hopeful. It will be called "It Doesn't Matter What Happens Next."

Sag Harbor Chanty

After the model is struck by lightning, she becomes really good at yoga. She teaches classes at the small studio by the harbor and afterwards has long talks in the parking lot with her students. She sees the way they stare at her, like any minute something might happen. And they all ask the same questions; they want to know if the current made her body bend better, or if she can feel things about the future. But all she knows is that she was struck by lightning and then she wasn't. Sometimes she wishes it had done what it was supposed to do, but she has never said this out loud. Her boyfriend makes jokes at parties about how the television reception is clearer now, or how he'll stand away from her when they walk in the rain. She doesn't really like him very much anymore. In horror movie storms, skinny bolts of lightning walk across the sky with the shuddering legs of a yearling, but she knows that's not how it really is. She remembers how it pushed against the night and lit up the sky's nervous system before it hit her. She remembers how it singled her out. In class a woman who was attacked by a shark shows her a scar that starts at her calf and gets wider as it winds up her waist. It's the first map of lightning she has ever seen and she can't turn away. The frayed fault line is like a fossil of electricity, evidence of a fever. In it she recognizes the turn and rip of the current, the break of a bite from nowhere—

Breaker's Kaddish

In 1983 ten members of the Israeli wrestling team were
killed when their driver slipped into a shallow sleep and
their van jumped the overpass, fell twenty-eight feet and
sunk into the ocean. Only Ziv Levy, who was sitting in the
front seat, survived. He went through the windshield and
landed safely on the sidewalk as the van disappeared
below. He had known his teammates all his life. He had
been to their Bar Mitzvahs, eaten endless meals with their
parents, and had even kissed some of their sisters in high
school. In spite of being 62-0, with no one ever even
coming close to beating him, the crash blew him out the
door and onto the road where there was nothing he could
do but listen to the van shoot through the air and
disappear under the waves. Lying on the asphalt, blood
spilled in and out of his mouth. Whenever he tried to
move, something in his shoulder kept breaking. The
bones of his wrists felt like boiling water. And yet, he
lived. It took months, but he came back stronger than
ever. He spent every day lifting weights, skipping and
wrestling the students from the university, who he beat so
quickly there wasn't even a name for it. He ate five meals
a day, filled with ancient grains and secret soups. He
spoke as little as possible. He started sleeping with
prostitutes. He felt depressed whenever he was buying
groceries and he found that no song on the radio could
make him feel anything anymore; he longed for the days
when a great chorus would leave him holding his side.
Late one night, while sitting outside a bar, he watches a
kid chase his girlfriend down to the water and his heart
feels like the wrong shape for his body. Sullen, dark and
dressed like caretakers, two fishermen pull nets from the
water and blare disco songs from a battered radio. Both
scenes scare him to death.

Why A Scar Is Better Than Being Good At Swordfighting

The soccer player who was bitten by a shark has a scar that sits under his eye like the fossil of a creature with a spine. Your friends think he gets all the girls because it makes him look tough, but you know that's not it. It's how they can see from the scar violence failed on him, how it could only manage to glide against his face in a weak splash. He kicks winning goals, he gets perfect grades and to make matters worse, he's a really nice guy. He's kind and thoughtful and speaks quietly as if he's discussing someone's terrible childhood. You make everyone laugh with impressions of your professors and your ventriloquist act with a sandwich, but that's about all you've got. You are old enough to understand that funny always loses to a scar. At night you stare in the mirror and think about giving yourself one, just to even things up. A quick swipe with a knife would last for years of girls, but you worry that you don't know how far to take the blade or if the bleeding will stop on its own. You'd probably go too deep, puncture an artery and soak the campus in blood; or you'd go too shallow for stitches and end up bandaged and embarrassed, known as a fraud forever. But the real problem is you wouldn't know how to live under a scar; how to act, how to stand, what to say when people say things. Instead you try to carve your initials in the wood frame above the window. As you slice away, the blade goes hot in your hand and the letters break in half on the surface of the grain. It looks like you're trying to tell a story you've never heard before.

Plane Crash, Full Moon, David Naughton, etc

Shelly Beecher was so metal, pregnant in 9th grade and smoking on the grass behind the lockers in her Iron Maiden t-shirt. Her boyfriend Tom Moody was a senior and he had muscles and a moustache and a car with no muffler that jackhammered across the parking lot every morning. One day in class you let her copy your *Great Expectations* quiz and after that you never saw her again. It didn't take long for Tom Moody to get a new girlfriend; she was blonde and wore dresses with skulls on them and when they kissed against his locker she'd put both her hands on his face. You hoped she would destroy him quickly. That night the moon did something it does every three thousand years, and the famous hard rock band were killed instantly when their tour bus flew off the freeway and exploded in an empty field behind the miniature golf course. On the news smoke tumbled from the twisted knots of scattered fuselage and firemen ran relays with hoses around giant burning dragons. The night was lit by ambulances as paramedics kneeled over bodies and policemen with pads took notes in front of a tennis shoe in the bushes. Across the back of a reporter, a girl in a bikini with wet black eyes wandered from a patch of smoking debris and walked around in circles in the ashy darkness. A few hours later, while cleaning your parents' pool you pulled a mouse from the drain and set it down in the grass. Crushed by the press of water, he gasped and steadied himself in the moonlight. You wanted him to dart back into the night but he didn't; he just stared straight ahead like he was waiting for you to do the same thing. You still can't remember who moved first.

Summer At Pitch 77

In late June at dusk, everyone was a silhouette playing
with a dog on their lawn. But when the daughter of the
doctor who invented that thing for the heart let the straps
of her dress fall off her shoulders, that's when the summer
finally started. When you got in a fight with the kid across
the street and he slashed your face with chickenwire, your
dad gave you a sip of brandy, wrapped your head in
gauze and the two of you sat on the couch playing chess
like a wounded Russian general and his trusty medic. You
were too young to be a contender, but you wanted her to
see you injured; you wanted to walk past her house the
next day, bandaged like the street celebrity. But Jack
Narobi, who played guitar on his driveway with a hazy
smile under feathered hair, stole the spotlight when he
got caught breaking into the sporting goods store and
dedicated his crime to her on the evening news. Even
though he ended up going to jail for seven months, you
wished you had thought of that. In July she worked for the
Senator and later she'd go to that college in
Massachusetts, but she would never come home again,
even when her dad did something else and television
cameras lined up outside their house for two days. You
spent the rest of August throwing things up and down the
street. You fell in love with Leslie Miley who moved from
Georgia and swam out back with your sister; you thought
maybe if you got hit by a car there was an outside chance
that she would be the one to love you. When the nights
grew shallow and school was about to start, you
wondered if in his cell Jack Narobi knew the season was
over, if he would lie in bed in the dark and listen to the
sounds of summer turn to static, feel the sticky press of his
shirt lifting behind his back.

Karina Around The Bend

And then July kicked into double overtime and the Danish
girl who rolled the kids of the cliff millionaires around the
country club snuck you through the window of the
Western Estate and taught you how to say *wolf*. In the
daytime she'd sit by the pool, soaking in the suburbs, and
you'd watch the tan settle on her skin like perfect
reception. At night you'd sit together on the steps of your
apartment and promise her you'd quit the job hitting
tennis balls under the skirts of average looking
housewives. While you talked about the next hundred
years, across the street at the auto repair the mechanics
would stumble out of the dead hot workshop, their sweat
pulling their shirts taut against their skin in perfect
silhouetted X-rays. She'd open the atlas and point to old
European cities, tell stories of her father forcing metal
together in the shipyard and her mother breaking her
ankle ice skating in the 1960 Olympics. While she slept
you imagined crouching in hollow horses in the shadows
of cold embassies. And you planned on breaking into the
furniture store, stealing couches and lamps and tables,
strapping them on your back like a Dr. Seuss character
and careening down a crooked hill to her, the mossy roofs
of the village leaning over the houses in soggy shadows.
Before people leave they say three things they don't
mean and one thing they forgot to tell you that changes
everything. She did all four at once. For the rest of the
summer you sat in the dark alone; the fracture in your
shoulder kept breaking over and over against your skin.
You could feel the dim glow the doctor showed you
stitching through the bone; it moved in a low, terrible
hum under the covers.

Blue Door Option

Everybody knew the magician was dying and this would be his last party. And it was too bad because all of his ex-girlfriends were there - even Stacey Mitchell, the news anchor who he had lived on a houseboat with when he held his breath for the whole summer. He was taking requests. He would do whatever we wanted. He would make birds explode from his chest, he would steal wallets from anyone in the room, he would build a house of cards on the back of his hands. All we had to do was ask. But no one did, because everyone was sure he would crack in the middle, fall to the floor and leave something suspended they could never fix. So instead of magic, he sang an old Nathan McCoy song about losing something in Hawaii. He had a falsetto you could feel across your shoulders. His hands were thin, he hadn't slept in two months, and you were the only one who knew a few weeks earlier he had parked his car somewhere and never saw it again. When he was too sick to come out for his own garage sale, he told you to give everything away. You watched people take his couch, his television, his doves, and you felt like you were officiating at a robbery. If you're a decent magician, he once told you, when you die people will miss you. But if you're a really great magician, they'll always think you're alive and in the middle of the best trick of all time. Even though you watched him fade in front of a machine, heard his breathing disappear like a radio station slipping off the air, you still look for him now. In the eyes of the teller at the bank, in the stands at minor league baseball games, in the credits of movies from Iceland--you suspect everyone. He was that good.

How To Get Mail In The Suburbs

When you are twelve your sister leaves town with the
mailman and the replacement guy gives everyone the
wrong mail. He is tough, he wears his hat low over his
eyes, and he never looks at anyone. He blares speed
metal and screeches through the neighborhood. Even
when you are underwater in the pool out back, you can
hear him shoving letters into the boxes like he's getting
back at someone for something. But no one ever
complains. After he drives away, people meet in the hush
of kitchens or the shadows of porches and give mail back
to each other. A year before, your sister didn't tell anyone
she moved in with Mark Jacobi and she ruined the whole
summer. Now she has ruined the neighborhood postal
system. And because they can't talk about daughters or
mail, your parents let you sort it out. Suddenly in your life
there are things like catalogs you know you should return
to the woman next door who was Miss Texas 1967, but you
are too stunned by the silver of the world inside to do it:
women on docks collecting flowers, men in great shoes
riding bicycles, couples leading quiet lives on boats. At
school, girls still don't like you but it doesn't keep you
from falling in love with Sarah Lindsor, whose father
invented a valve for the heart. She took it to class for
"Something I Learned About My Parents" and when she
held it up it looked thin and small like something that
goes inside a puppet. After school, you take the long way
home so you can pass by her street. The mailman there is
different - he is tanned and elegant and places letters in
boxes as if they were things made of glass. You can't
remember what your old mailman looked like. Sometimes
you can't remember what your sister looked like, either.
She has dark hair. She has boyfriends who fix cars. She
never writes letters. The new mailman is thick and
dangerous; every day he attacks the route in vicious
bursts, like a slalom skier making diagonal strikes around
the gates. Behind him boxes dangle off their wooden
posts and vibrate meekly. He is reckless and terrible
every single time you see him. He is the only person you
trust.

Shark Nocturne

In July the summer turns to sharks. Signs from years ago
with missing letters offer warnings, but the swimmer who
has been training in open water for the Olympics decides
to keep going. She has world records and she's been in
magazines, the glowing medals of an aquatic admiral
around her neck, but every morning when she steps off
the beach into the surf, she knows none of that matters.
With every stroke the waves roll drowsily over her in
deep, plangent bass notes; they brush against her
earplugs like a distant calypso song. Underneath her the
split bones of coral rise from the ocean floor like miles of
drowned suburbs. Her boyfriend, the champion
skateboarder, shows her documentaries of sharks ripping
at surfers and slashing at cages, their jaws fireworks of
bloody teeth, but it's no use—nothing can talk her out of
the water. He has bad dreams, complains to his friends,
sees a psychiatrist who is saturated with understanding.
One morning when he is watering the lawn he finally
thinks *mayday*. Above him a plane passes like a dial tone;
long and luxurious it rolls through the wires; a skimming
sonance, a floating frequency, the long breath before an
emergency.

Night Shift Superstar

Late at night and pretty nuts, you walk the dark surf with
the girl from Huxton, the southern syrup so thick every
step seems stuck to the map. She holds your hand and
tells you about the accident: the surfer, the sharks, the
actor's boat, the fire. How she watched the divers lower
themselves into the water like burglars through windows
like whispers. She says someone is already writing a
book. It's going to be called *Throat Made Of Stars*. She
says there will be a movie but it won't be called that. It
has been a terrible summer but at least everyone died
quickly. Across the street at the Meseneja resort the
nightwatchman juggles flashlights. Their beams glide
through the darkness like the leftover parts of a good
idea; the hiss before they fall back into his hands is a
voice whispering, *California*.